BOOK 2

HEADWORK

Chris Culshaw and Deborah Waters

OXFORD UNIVERSITY PRESS

Oxford University Press, Walton Street, Oxford OX2 6DP

Oxford   New York   Toronto
Delhi   Bombay   Calcutta   Madras   Karachi
Petaling Jaya   Singapore   Hong Kong   Tokyo
Nairobi   Dar es Salaam   Cape Town
Melbourne   Auckland

and associated companies in
Berlin   Ibadan

Oxford is a trade mark of Oxford University Press

© Oxford University Press 1984

First published 1984

Reprinted 1984, 1985, 1987, 1988, 1990, 1991
ISBN 0 19 833373 0

Illustrations are by Andy Bylo,
Marie-Hélène Jeeves, Hugh Marshall,
David Murray, and Ursula Sieger

The cover illustration is by
Marie-Hélène Jeeves

Typeset in Great Britain by
Rowland Phototypesetting Ltd
Bury St Edmunds, Suffolk
and printed by
Scotprint, Musselburgh

CONTENTS

Headwork is based on the following assumptions:

> that we learn to read by reading;
>
> that reading is in essence a problem solving process;
>
> that different types of reading matter demand different strategies.

The books have been written to help pupils find a challenge in the necessary routine of practising basic reading skills and to help them understand that reading involves thinking. We have therefore tried to balance readability against "thinkability" and posed demanding questions in an interesting but readable way.

Most of the tasks have a puzzle element and often ask the pupil to read with a specific question in mind. Some ask the learner to restructure what s/he has read by changing text into drawing. Some demand comparison between pictures or between texts. Some require summaries. Others involve sequencing. Many are designed to develop skills of classification and introduce different ways of tabulating information.

While many of the tasks lead to clear-cut, short (often single word) written answers, others are more open-ended and ask the pupil to use such concepts as "true", "false" and "not enough evidence". These open-ended tasks lend themselves to oral work in pairs or in small groups.

There is constant repetition of basic sight words and concepts including colours, shapes, parts of the body, and terms that define position in time and space such as *over*, *under*, *next to*, *before*, *after*, *right*, *left*, etc.

In compiling *Headwork* we have been concerned above all to help learners in their efforts to *comprehend* what they read. So, text is supported with pictures and diagrams and new and difficult words are introduced in meaningful contexts.

"Readability" measures have many shortcomings and do not always do justice to the subtlety of the reading process. It is difficult to say exactly what makes a text readable and comprehensible: factors such as syntax, topic, concept loading, the match between the text and the readers' prior knowledge all play a part. Simple texts, with strictly controlled vocabulary, are not always the easiest to read with understanding. What is more, such texts offer very little challenge and may well defeat our ends for they are unlikely to get our pupils reading and *re-reading* in their efforts to search for meaning. There must be some challenge, some puzzlement and intellectual demand if the pupil is to develop into a reflective reader.

The table shows the major skills practised by each task. This is a broad categorization as the categories often overlap. For example, many of the matching tasks also require sequencing skills. The table also identifies those tasks which need a lot of teacher input, both in starting the learners off and in discussing their answers.

Major skills emphasized	page number
Cloze	15, 18, 20, 24
Drawing from text	8, 40, ⑤⑧, ⑤⑨
Matching	6, 10, 19, **25**, 32–33, **39**, ④②–④③, **60–61**
Deduction	**12**, 30–31, 36, 41, 44–45, 46–47, ⑤③
Sequencing	26, 34
Classification	7, 11, 14, 16–17, ②①, ②⑦, **35**, **37**, ④②–④③, 48–49
Flow charts	**28–29**
Homonyms	**52**
Summary	**56–57**, **62–63**
Solving riddles	③⑧, 51
Comparisons	22–23, **50**, 54–55, **64**
Using vowels	9, 13

Numbers printed in **bold** indicate tasks needing a lot of teacher explanation.
Numbers circled indicate tasks with open-ended outcomes and a number of possible answers.

A

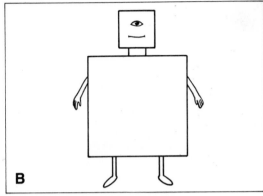

B

C

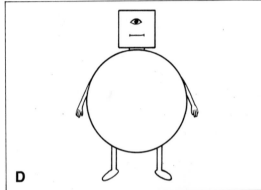

D

What to do

Pug, Mug, Bug and Tug are Martians.
Which is which?   Match the pictures with the words.
Write your answers like this: *1. C*

1.   Pug has a round body and a round head.

2.   Mug has a square body and round head.

3.   Bug has a round body and a square head.

4.   Tug has a square body and a square head.

What to do next

Draw and label four more creatures from Mars.
Use these words: red, yellow, green, blue, square, round, oblong, triangular.

What to do

Copy the chart.   Fill it in.   The first row has been done for you.

---

	dog A	dog B	dog C
tall	✓	✓	✗
short legs			
long legs			
long hair			
short hair			
tall and thin			

What to do next

Collect three pictures of cars or of horses.   Make a chart like the one for the dogs.

CLASSIFICATION

What to do

The Ugs are a family of space monsters.   Read their descriptions.   Then draw and label them.

Fred Ug lives on Pluto.   He has a body like an apple.   He has a long thin neck.   His head is square.

He has six blue legs.

His head is red and his body is green.

Mary Ug is Fred's sister.   She lives on Venus.   Her body is like a pear.   She has a very long thin neck.

Her head is round.   She has three big eyes.   She has no mouth and no nose.   She has lots of orange hair.

She has thin green arms: They grow out of her head!

Mary's six legs are blue.   Her feet are purple.   Each foot has three sharp toes.

What to do next

Write a description of Fred's pet.   Use these words (and any others):

red	fire	twenty
head	square	legs
tail	round	dots
claws	eyes	high

Draw Fred's pet and label it.

What to do

All the vowels have been missed out of this story. Copy the story.
Put in the missing letters.

P_m w_nt f_sh_ng _n th_ p_rk. Sh_ p_t s_m_

br__d _n h_r h__k. Sh_ d_d n_t c_tch _ny f_sh

b_c__se th_ d_cks g_t _ll h_r b__t.

What to do next

Pam meets the park-keeper.   Write what they say.

Park-keeper: Can't you read ?
Pam:
Park-keeper:
Pam:

USING VOWELS

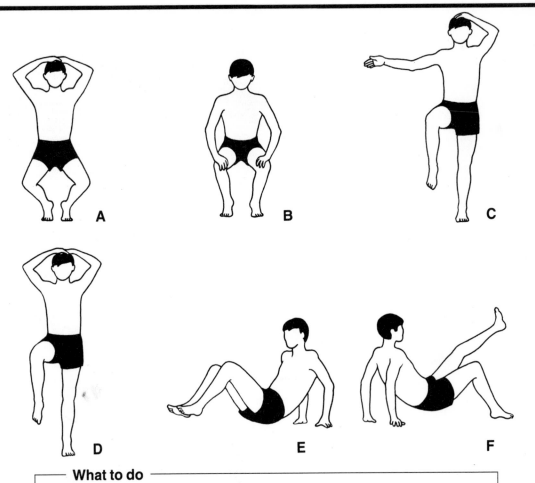

What to do

Match the pictures with the words.   Write your answers like this: *1. D*

1. Stand on one leg.   Put both hands on your head.
2. Sit on the floor.   Put both hands on the floor.   Lift up both legs.
3. Bend both your knees.   Put both your hands on your head.
4. Stand on one leg.   Put one hand on your head.
5. Bend both your knees.   Put your hands on your knees.
6. Sit on the floor. Put both hands on the floor. Lift one leg in the air.

What to do next

Draw some stick men in different positions.
Write a description for each one.

A

B

C

What to do

Copy the chart.　Fill it in.

---

	face A	face B	face C
thin lips	✓	✓	✗
curly hair			
glasses			
hat			
large round eyes			
thin nose			
long eye lashes			
round head			
ear rings			

What to do next

Draw a face with thin lips, long hair, a beard and glasses.

CLASSIFICATION

Betty is helping her dad.   She wants to be a carpenter when she leaves school.   Blackie the cat is watching them work.

What to do

True? (T) False? (F) Not enough evidence? (NEE)
Which sentence is true?   Which is false?
Sometimes there is not enough evidence to tell.
Write your answers like this: *1. True*

1. Betty's dad is right handed.
2. Betty is left handed.
3. Betty is holding the hammer.
4. Blackie is under the chair.
5. There are three pictures on the wall.
6. Betty helps her dad every week-end.

7. Betty is wearing glasses.
8. The cat is watching Betty's dad.
9. Betty is taller than her dad.
10. There are five nails on the carpet.

DEDUCTION

What to do

All the vowels have been missed out of this story. Copy the story and put in the missing letters.

P_m's h__s_ w_s _n f_r_. Sh_ r_ng f_r th_ f_r_ br_g_d_ .

P_m w_s st_ck _n h_r b_dr__m.

Sh_ c__ld _p_n th_ w_nd_w b_t sh_ c__ld n_t g_t __t.

"J_mp!" sh.__t_d th_ f_r_m_n.

P_m j_mp_d. Sh_ l_nd_d _n th_ m_n. Sh_ w_s s_f_, b_t th_ f_r_m_n h_d t_ g_ t_ h_sp_t_l!

What to do next

Pam went to see the fireman in hospital. Write down what they said.

Pam: Hello, how are you feeling?
Fireman:
Pam:

A

B

C

What to do

Copy the chart.   Fill it in.   The first row has been done for you.

	bird A	bird B	bird C
black head	✓	✗	✗
long legs			
sharp claws			
long neck			
webbed feet			
short beak			
big ears			
long black neck			
short tail feathers			
short legs			

What to do next

Draw a bird with long black legs, a black head, spots, webbed feet and a long tail.
Collect three pictures of animals or bikes.   Make a chart like the one for the birds.

CLASSIFICATION

What to do

Think of a word that fits each blank space.
Lots of words can fit.   Write down the number and the word you choose.

This is a story about the _____1_____ at the High School.   One day a _____2_____ put some blue ink into the pool.

All the kids who _____3_____ for a swim turned blue.

Their faces went _____4_____, their teeth went blue, their _____5_____ went blue, their eyes went blue _____6_____ their ears went blue.   They looked like _____7_____ from Star Trek.

The next day the _____8_____ boy put a SHARK in the pool.   The shark _____9_____ all the boys and girls.   The _____10_____ was full of arms and legs and blood, and heads, and empty swimming costumes, and _____11_____

The _____12_____ in the pool went red.

CLOZE

Which witch is which?

What to do

Copy this part of the table and fill it in.

		witch A	witch B	witch C
1. a watch	1	✗	✓	✗
2. empty hands	2			
3. a long nose	3			
4. a broom stick	4			
5. glasses	5			
6. hairy legs	6			
7. a dress with flowers	7			
8. a walking stick	8			
9. a cooking pot	9			
10. a bent black hat	10			
11. pointed ears	11			
12. a frog	12			
13. buttons	13			
14. a hat band	14			
15. a watch and a broom stick and hairy legs	15			
16. a pointed hat and pointed shoes and big ears	16			

A

B

C

What to do

Think of a word that fits each blank space.   Write down each number and the word you choose.   Lots of words can fit.

Jo had a radio.   She got it in a jumble sale.   It was a very strange radio.

One day when Jo was listening to the six o'clock   1   a very strange thing happened.   A hand came   2   of the radio and got hold of Jo's face.   Jo was very   3   .   She   4   the comic she was reading.   She   5   her cup of tea off the arm of her chair.

Jo picked up the   6   .   She stared at it.   Then the   7   came out again.   This time it got hold of Jo's left   8   .   Jo jumped back.   Jo got very upset.   She grabbed the radio and ran into the kitchen.   She put the radio in the sink and turned on   9   taps.   The water filled the sink.   Jo heard a voice coming from the radio.   It said, "Help me! Help me! . . .   Please help me.   I'm   10   ."

What to do

Can you match the speech balloons with the places?

Write your answers like this: **1.**D

1. Where are the cornflakes please?

2. Is this song in the Top Ten ?

3. Have you got a can of Coke please ?

4. How did he break his leg ?

5. Did you bring your fishing rod ?

6. Let's get out of here !

7. Will it bite me ?

8. That's my desk. I always sit there.

places

A. fish and chip shop

B. doctor's

C. classroom

D. supermarket

E. vet's

F. disco

G. park

H. Dracula's Castle

MATCHING

What to do

Think of a word that fits each space.   Write the numbers and the word you choose.

Bert and Flert are billiard balls.   They are   1   .   They are the same   2   as an orange.   They live in the pockets of a billiard table.   The table has   3   cloth on it.   Bert and Flert like to   4   about on the cloth.   It is very smooth.

One day Mr Thumper came into the club.   Bert and   5   did not like Mr Thumper.   Mr Thumper was a very bad player.   He hit the balls   6   hard.   If you hit billiard balls too hard they   7   off the table.

Bert and Flert   8   to play a trick on Mr Thumper.   Every time Mr Thumper tried to hit them they   9   out of the way.   They   10   in the pockets and under the table.   Mr Thumper got cross. He jumped   11   the table and ran after Bert and Flert.   His heavy   12   made marks on the cloth.   The manager of the   13   threw him out.   He was never   14   back in the club.

What to do

How would you feel if you said these things?
Copy the table. Just write the numbers. Put a tick where you think it fits best.

			Copy this part and fill it in.		
			happy	normal	sad
1.	I had a great school dinner today	1	✓		
2.	My best friend wouldn't talk to me today.	2			
3.	My mum gave me a pound.	3			
4.	Can I have a plaster?	4			
5.	Can I have my prize?	5			
6.	There are 33 people in my class.	6			
7.	My mum made me eat all my dinner.	7			
8.	It's my birthday tomorrow.	8			
9.	What time is it?	9			
10.	I can't come out. I've got to tidy my bedroom.	10			
11.	I can't come to detention. I've got to go to my gran's.	11			
12.	It is a girl.	12			

CLASSIFICATION

picture A

What to do

In which picture can you spot these things?
Write your answers by making a table like this:

	picture A	picture B
1	✓	✓
2		
3		
4		
5		
6		
7		

1. a monster with a long thin neck
2. a monster with a long thin spotted neck
3. a monster with a head like a television set
4. a monster with sharp teeth
5. a monster with one tooth
6. a monster with no teeth
7. a monster with square eyes

COMPARISONS

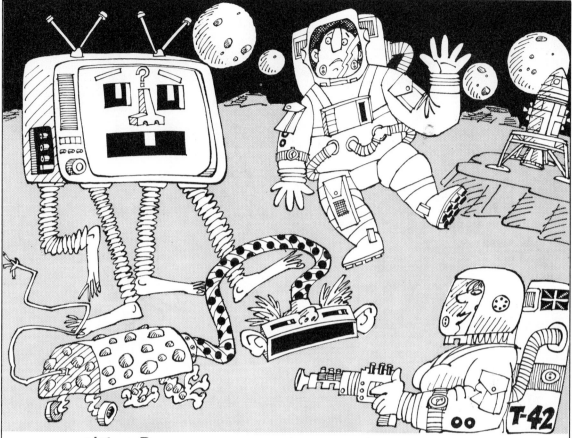

picture B

What to do next

Make a second table like this:
---

	picture A	picture B
8		
9		
10		
11		
12		
13		
14		
15		

8. a monster with a plug on its tail
9. a monster with four wheels
10. a monster with bare feet
11. four moons in the sky
12. two spaceships
13. two spacemen
14. a spacewoman with a gun
15. a spaceman without a gun

COMPARISONS

What to do

Think of a word that fits each space.   Write the number and the word you choose.   Lots of words can fit.

My uncle is a very   1   fellow.   He eats dinosaurs and drinks   2   .   He wears very silly clothes.   He wears a thing like a   3   made of dinosaur skin.   He carries a   4   made from a tree trunk.   He   5   wears shoes.   People complain because   6   feet are smelly.   They give him shoes but he   7   them or uses them for cups.

His hair   8   a mile long.   Last week it was eaten by an ant-eater.   It   9   it up just like a vacuum cleaner.

Uncle Bob has very   10   eye sight.   But he cannot get any glasses to   11   him.   He has one eye in the   12   of his forehead.

I have a problem.   I do   13   know what to buy him for his birthday.   He   14   he wants an electric razor but I   15   he needs a lawn mower.

What to do

Which words go in which balloons?
Write your answers like this:

A. *What are you doing?*
B.

1. I don't know.
2. Help!
3. What are you doing?
4. I thought you said bird watching was safe.
5. Bird watching.
6. What kind of bird is it?

What to do next

Draw the next two pictures in the story and write the words in the speech balloons.

MATCHING

What to do

These four sets of sentences make a story.
Put them in the right order.

A. He lay in his car.   The farmer's wife was having a baby.

B. One day last week someone left a gate open.   A cow got on to the lane.

C. The farmer had to help her.   The doctor did not come in time.

D. The doctor's car hit it and crashed.   He was hurt.

What to do

How would you feel if you said these things?
Copy the table.   Just write the numbers.   Put a tick where you think it fits best.

		Copy this part and fill it in.			
		happy	sad	angry	frightened
1.	What was that noise?	1				✓
2.	My granny used to live in that house.	2				
3.	. . . and then a big hand came and grabbed the baby.	3				
4.	Oh! No! I've broken the window.	4				
5.	What a big ice cream!	5				
6.	He's bigger than I am.	6				
7.	You've just eaten my dinner!	7				
8.	I've got masses of homework.	8				
9.	We've lost.	9				
10.	Did you see that? It's a ghost.	10				
11.	What sharp teeth it's got.	11				
12.	She wouldn't come out with me.	12				
13.	I've got a bite.	13				
14.	I laughed until I cried.	14				
15.	I've lost that horrible coat Granny gave me.	15				

CLASSIFICATION

Jim is a robot.   He cannot think for himself.   You have to tell him what to do.

Here are his instructions.   They tell him how to wash a plate.

What to do

What is missed out of Box A?
Write out the complete chart.

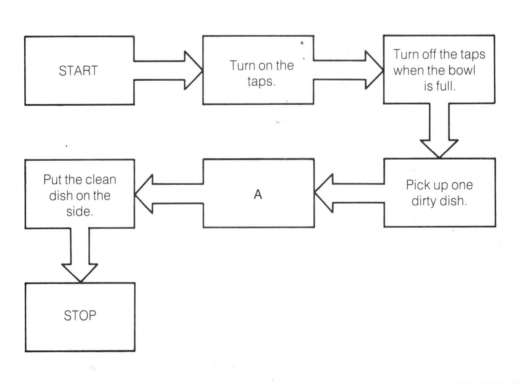

START → Turn on the taps. → Turn off the taps when the bowl is full.

Put the clean dish on the side. ← A ← Pick up one dirty dish.

STOP

Here are the robot's instructions for lighting a fire.   What is missing out of Box A?

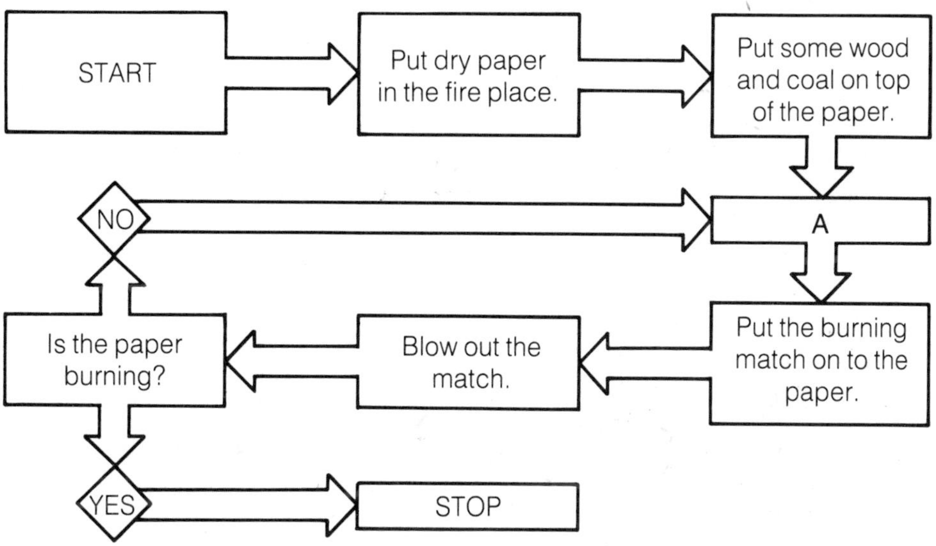

START	Put dry paper in the fire place.

Put some wood and coal on top of the paper.

NO

A

Is the paper burning?

Blow out the match.

Put the burning match on to the paper.

YES → STOP

Jim works in a light bulb factory.   He checks the bulbs. What is missing from Box A and Box B?

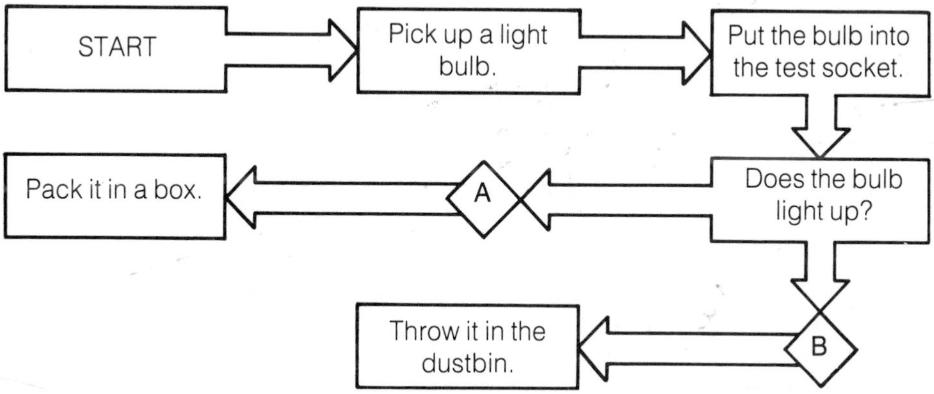

START → Pick up a light bulb. → Put the bulb into the test socket.

Pack it in a box. ← A ← Does the bulb light up?

Throw it in the dustbin. ← B

Make up a flow chart which tells Jim how to clean your shoes.

FLOW CHARTS

What to do

True? (T) False? (F) Not enough evidence? (NEE)
Write your answers like this: *1. True*

1. The picture fell on Betty.
2. Her dad fell off the chair.
3. The nail hit a hot water pipe.
4. The cat got wet.
5. Betty's hair got wet.
6. The picture fell on the cat.
7. The glass in the picture cracked.
8. The string holding up the picture broke.
9. Betty's dad hurt his hand.
10. Betty's jacket got wet.
11. The wallpaper got wet.
12. Betty's dad shouted, "Look out Betty!"
13. Betty was holding the hammer.
14. The cat made Betty's dad fall.
15. The picture fell on Betty's dad.

What to do next

Now write more sentences about the picture:
  two true sentences (T)
  two false sentences (F)
  two 'not enough evidence' sentences (NEE)

DEDUCTION

What to do

Sally is blind.   She uses sounds to help her to find her way.   Pick the **ten** sounds she **probably** heard when she walked round the paddling pool.

Write your answers like this: *1. water splashing*

a)   low flying jets

b)   water splashing

c)   ducks

d)   a horse

e)   a Radio 1 D.J.

f)   glass breaking

g)   someone playing a piano

h)   someone striking a match

MATCHING

i)	a door bell	o)	a child crying
j)	a cat hissing	p)	owls
k)	a telephone	q)	someone snoring
l)	a motorbike	r)	someone chopping wood
m)	someone sawing wood	s)	roller skates
n)	heavy rain	t)	milk bottles rattling

What to do

These six sets of sentences make a story.
Put them in the right order.

A. Harry woke up.   He stamped on the rags but he could not put them out.

B. He fell asleep.   He had been smoking.   His cigarette fell onto his newspaper.

C. Harry could not get help.   He died in the fire.

D. Harry was a night watchman.   He worked in a paint factory.

E. Harry was trapped.   The phone wires were burned.

F. It started to burn.   It set fire to some old rags.

What to do next

You are a policewoman/policeman or a fireman.
Draw a plan of the room and the things in it.   Label them.
Say what you think happened.

We asked 10 pupils about their pets.   This is what they said:

1.   A cat is a very good pet for an old person.
2.   I don't like dogs.   They frighten me.
3.   Rabbits are cheap and easy to look after.
4.   It costs a lot to keep a pony.
5.   It is wrong to put animals in cages.
6.   Black cats bring you good luck.
7.   Goldfish need fresh water every week.
8.   Kittens mess up your furniture.
9.   Cats are very intelligent.
10.   Snakes are good pets because they are easy to look after.

	A good things about pets	B bad things about pets	C looking after a pet	D pets and children
1	✓			
2				
3				
4				
5				
6				
7				
8				
9				
10				

What to do

Copy the table.
Classify the 10 answers.   The first one has been done for you.
Sometimes you may want to tick more than one column.

CLASSIFICATION

What to do

True? (T) False? (F) Not enough evidence? (NEE)
Write your answers like this: **1.True**

1. Betty is holding the telephone.
2. Her dad is trying to save the cat.
3. The cat is trying to keep dry.
4. The telephone will not work.
5. Betty's hair is still dry.
6. Her dad's shoes are full of water.
7. The cat cannot swim.
8. All Betty's clothes are very wet.
9. Her dad is stopping the water with his little finger.
10. His pullover is not wet.
11. The cat wants to sit on Betty's shoulders.
12. The water has covered the carpet.
13. Betty's hands are cold.
14. Her dad's right arm is very tired.
15. Betty is trying to ring the plumber.
16. Betty's dad is very happy.
17. The water is coming from a broken gutter.
18. The water is dripping off Betty's chin.
19. The cat is watching Betty look for the hammer.
20. Betty's mum has gone to get help.

DEDUCTION

I haven't any pockets

We asked 10 pupils about their pocket money.
This is what they said:

1. I have to do jobs for my pocket money.
2. I get 50p from my mum and 50p from my dad.
3. Most of my pocket money goes on records.
4. My pocket money never lasts until the end of the week.
5. I put my pocket money in the post office.
6. My mum is out of work, so we don't get much pocket money.
7. My gran gives me pocket money and so does my dad.
8. I don't like having to ask for pocket money.   I'd rather have a job and earn it.
9. My big sister gives me a £1 if I tidy her garage.
10. We've got a big family so I don't get much pocket money.

	jobs and pocket money	how much pocket money	parents and pocket money	spending pocket money
1	✓			
2				
3				
4				
5				
6				
7				
8				
9				
10				

What to do

Copy the table.
Classify the 10 answers.
The first one has been done for you.

CLASSIFICATION

What to do

What do you think the word *it* means in these sentences?
Different people will have different ideas.
Write down your answers beside each number.

1. It is too blunt to cut the padlock.
2. Be careful. It will boil over.
3. The wind blew it across to the next island.
4. By morning it had covered the garden.
5. It was washed up on the beach last week – what a smell!
6. It must be broken.   It prints an A instead of an E.
7. It is too thin . . .   I can see blood coming through.
8. It is not worth £10 because the gears are broken.
9. It is an hour late because of the snow.
10. They could not get it up the stairs so they took it to bits.
11. They could not get it up the stairs so they had to send it back.
12. It came off in his hand so he was trapped inside.
13. It changed into a man in a black cloak.
14. She lost it down a drain so the other one is no use now.
15. Put it on the operating table, nurse.

What to do

Which words go in which balloons?
Write each letter and the words that fit that balloon.

1. This creature is very tall.

2. It has got white eyes at this end.

3. Do you think there is life on this planet?

4. What is that creature saying?

5. I don't know. Let's take a look.

6. I don't know. I can't understand it.

7. Yes and it is very thin too.

8. It has got red eyes at this end.

What to do next

Now draw the next pictures in the story. The visitors go into a launderette.

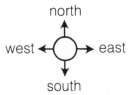

┌─ **What to do** ──────────────┐
│ Draw the island, using the key. │
└────────────────────────────────┘

1. The island is shaped like a skull.
2. Nobody lives on the island now but there is a ruined village in the middle. The village has nine small houses and a church.
3. On the coast north of the village there is a pier.
4. There is an unfenced road running from the village to the pier.
5. Just south of the village there is a small lake.
6. There is a stream coming out of the lake. It runs out into the sea on the west coast.
7. South of the village, near the sea, there is an old gold mine.
8. A railway line runs along the west coast from the mine to the pier.
9. The railway line crosses the stream by a small bridge.
10. There is a marsh along the east coast of the island.
11. On the south coast of the island there is a lighthouse.
12. There is a footpath from the church to the lighthouse.
13. There are two lots of cliffs. Some are east of the pier and some are west of the lighthouse.

key

house	▬		
church	♀	gold mine	▲
pier	⊥	railway	▬▭▬
unfenced road	⋯	bridge	▐█▌
stream	∿	lighthouse	⌂
lake	⌒	footpath	⋯
marsh	≡	cliffs	∿∿∿

DRAWING

What to do next

Where on your island would you expect to find these things?
Mark them on your map with their numbers.

1. a large pile of coal
2. an old bible
3. an eagle's nest
4. rushes
5. potatoes growing
6. a sign saying DANGER
7. a rusty bell
8. a safe

9. a safety helmet
10. a duck's nest
11. a pick and a shovel
12. a pile of rusty tins
13. bits of a rusty water-wheel
14. an old grave-stone
15. an old tin bath

DEDUCTION

Which of these items would you have in a survival kit?   You can only take *12*.

A.   a ball of string

B.   a file

C.   a magnifying glass

D.   a packet of pins

E.   a tooth-brush

F.   chewing gum

G.   a book

H.   a sharp knife

I.   a large plastic bag

J.   a walking stick

K.   a spade

L.   a length of hose pipe

M.   a pair of scissors

N.   a strong rope

O.   a watch

P.   a radio

Q.   a packet of seeds

R.   a first aid kit

S.   a balloon

T.   a pencil

U.   a spare pair of shoes

V.   matches

W.   a guitar

X.   a saw

What to do

Make your list like this and rate each item: *** very important
** quite important
* fairly important

	my 12 items for my survival kit	my ratings
1	first aid kit	***
2		
3		
4		
5		
6		
7		
8		
9		
10		
11		
12		

What to do

Which of the objects on the list (A–X) would you use to do these jobs?

1. start a fire in the rain
2. make some fish hooks
3. collect some rain water
4. kill a snake
5. catch a wild pig

6. signal to a passing ship
7. mend a bucket, if you had one
8. sharpen a saw
9. signal a passing plane
10. climb a palm tree to get coconuts

What to do next

How would you use a guitar to trap a wild goat?
Write your answers in sentences and draw some diagrams to go with them.

I'D NEVER SURVIVE ON A DESERT ISLAND... I HATE

MATCHING/CLASSIFICATION

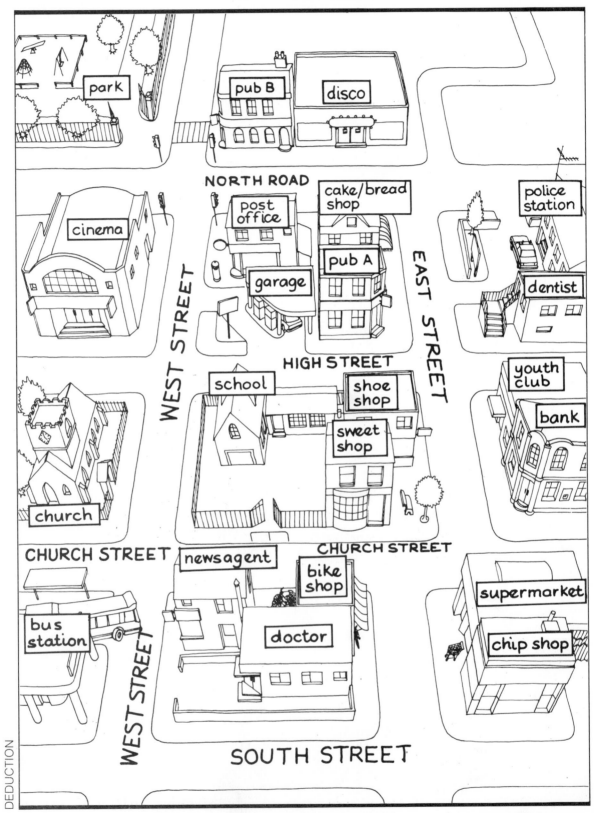

True? (T) False? (F) Not enough evidence? (NEE)
Write your answer like this: 1. *True*

1. The bank is on East Street.
2. The post office is on the corner of North Road and West Street.
3. The church is opposite the school.
4. The cinema is next to a pub.
5. East Street is a one way street.
6. There are lots of bikes behind the bike shop.
7. The disco is near the supermarket.
8. There is a trolley in front of the chip shop.
9. The bike shop is opposite the bank.
10. The youth club is in the same street as pub A.
11. There is a car park behind the supermarket.
12. There are two police cars in front of the police station.
13. The entrance to the school is on Church Street.
14. The bus is going to go along the High Street.
15. The bus station is a long way from the dentist.
16. The chip shop is very busy in the evening.
17. It takes fifteen minutes to get from the supermarket to the park.
18. If you walk from the shoe shop to the disco you pass the doctor's.
19. If you go from the church to the youth club you must cross West Street.
20. You have to cross two streets to get from the post office to the newsagent.

DEDUCTION

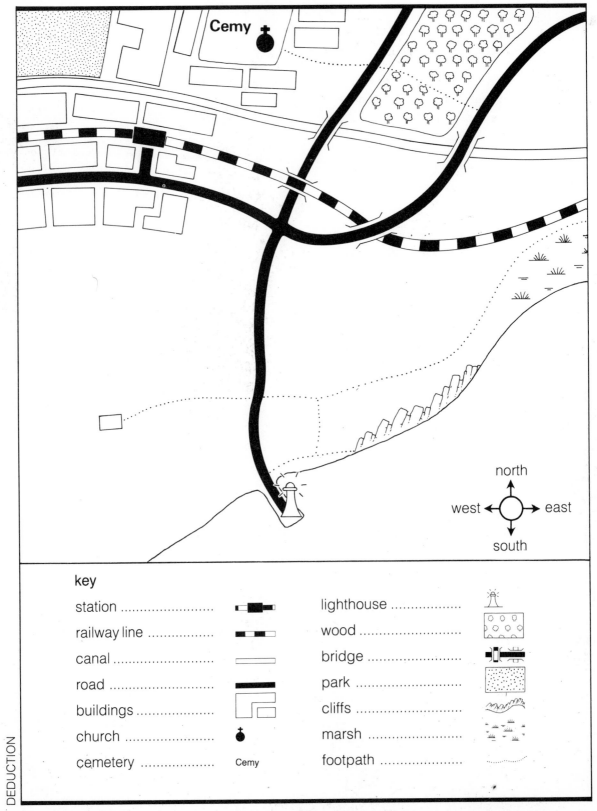

key

station		lighthouse	
railway line		wood	
canal		bridge	
road		park	
buildings		cliffs	
church		marsh	
cemetery	Cemy	footpath	

DEDUCTION

1. The railway line crosses the canal.
2. There are two bridges over the canal.
3. Many people have fallen down the cliffs.
4. The railway line goes over two roads.
5. The park is west of the church.
6. It takes half an hour to walk from the lighthouse to the cliffs.
7. You have to cross the road when you walk from the lighthouse to the cliffs.
8. The lighthouse is north of the church.
9. You cannot drive from the cliffs to the marsh.
10. There is a footpath from the church through the woods.
11. There is a sweet shop near the railway line.
12. You turn left at the crossroads when you drive from the lighthouse to the railway station.

What to do next

If you were going to build a supermarket, a caravan park, a petrol station and a sweet shop – where would you build them?
Give your reasons for putting them there.

DEDUCTION

normal   surprised   angry   happy   sad   puzzled

What to do

How are Pam and John feeling when they speak? Write your answers like this: *1. Normal*

John	Hello Pam. Where are you going?
Pam	To the dentist.
J	Have you got a bad tooth?
P	No – I am meeting my sister there. She had to go for a check-up.
J	Do you like your sister?
P	You must be joking! ②
J	I wish I had a sister.
P	Why?
J	I don't like being an only child. I get lonely.
P	Do you want to come to our house to play?
J	Yes please. ④
P	I've got a C.B. rig in my bedroom.
J	Wow! Your own rig? ⑤

CLASSIFICATION

P Yes – you can have a go on it if you want.

J Thanks.

P What's your handle?

J What?

P What's your C.B. nickname?

J I haven't got one.

P I think you should call yourself Tom Thumb because you're so small.

J Don't be cheeky!　I hate it when people say that!

P Where are you going?　Come back.　I didn't mean it.

J Oh yes you did!　I'm going to get my big brother to bash you.

P Don't tell lies!　You haven't got a brother.

What to do next

Make up the conversations between these people.

THEY LOOK LIKE TWINS BUT ARE THEY?

What to do

Say if these pairs of sentences have the same or different meanings.

1. Pam is good at woodwork and so is her mum.
   Pam and her mum are both good at woodwork.

2. The bus came late because of the snow.
   The bus was stuck in the snow.

3. The floor was wet because the sink was blocked.
   Water ran out of the blocked sink onto the floor.

4. The clock is always fast or slow.
   The clock never tells the right time.

5. The horse was in the field behind the barn.
   The horse was near the field behind the barn.

6. The boy climbed up the tree and got stuck.
   The boy could not get down from the tree.

7. The knife fell off the table onto Tom's foot and cut it.
   Tom cut his foot when he stood on a sharp knife.

8. Mary tried to mend her bike but did not have enough tools.
   Mary could not mend her bike because she did not have her tools.

9. Helen said, "I got lost because it was very foggy."
   "I did not know where I was in the fog," said Helen.

10. "I have seen this film before," said Pam.
    Pam said, "I know what this film is about."

What to do

Here are some clues.   What are these things?

1. They grow.
   They are dead.
   We have millions.
   We lose them when we get
      old.
   They go grey.

2. It is very big.
   A person could never stand
      on it.
   It is far, far, far, away.
   It can be life or death.
   It makes shadows.

3. It is made of metal.
   You can find it in the kitchen.
   We use it at meal times.
   It has four sharp ends.

4. It hangs in the air.
   It can be dangerous.
   It has wires going to it.
   It helps us to see.

5. It is flat.
   It opens.
   It has the world inside.
   It has a spine.

6. We sit on it.
   It has four legs.
   It has a tail.
   It is made of wood.
   It goes backwards and
      forwards.

7. It has four wheels.
   It is usually white.
   It moves about.
   It carries sick people.
   It is flat.
   You push or pull it.

8. It can be many colours.
   It gets smaller as it gets older.
   It can be hot or cold.
   It is made from string and wax.

9. It floats on water.
   You can see through it.
   It can melt.
   Skaters need it.

10. It is metal.
    It is bent.
    It is easy to put in.
    It is hard to get out.
    Fish hate it.

What to do next

Write some clues for these objects:
light bulb, bike pump, comb, a stool, baby's cot.

My Grandma

My grandma owned a lot of **land** near a **train** station. She was very rich when she died. Before her death she said to me:

"I **will** leave you my **record** collection.
It is very valuable."

After the funeral a big black box came in the **post**. There was a strange **cross** on the box, and a sign on the lid that looked like a **fly**. I opened the box. A white shiny **rock fell** out onto the carpet.

My mum made me put the box in the **yard**. The box was full of rock samples. What had happened to the record collection?

My Uncle Fred

My uncle Fred was a **train** driver. One day he made a plane without an engine. It looked like a bike with wings. He wanted to set a **record** for man-powered flight.

The first time he tried to **fly** the plane, the back wheel hit a **rock**. The plane broke. It took Fred six weeks to mend it in his **yard**.

Fred went in for a race. He had to **cross** the sea. This was dangerous because Fred could not swim. Just as Fred was nearing the winning **post**, he got cramp. His plane **fell** from the sky. He could not find a safe place to **land**. Uncle Fred was killed. He left me his plane in his **will**.

What to do

Copy this table.
Say if these words are used with the *same* or *different* meanings in the two stories.

	same	different
land		
train		
will		
record		
post		
cross		
fly		
rock		
fell		
yard		

HOMONYMS

What to do

Where would you see these signs?

1 MIND YOUR HEAD

2 Please do not talk.

3 PRESS TWICE

4 Leave your watch here.

5 Boys to the left | Girls to the right

6 We open at 9.00a.m. on wet days.

7 HAM CHEESE

8 All visitors must wear dark glasses

9 NO HIGH HEELS PLEASE

10 NO MORE THAN 3 PEOPLE AT A TIME

11 Press to open Turn to close

12 DO NOT TAP ON THE GLASS

13 Insert 10p when light flashes.

14 Next water 100km. Fill up now.

15 All passengers for Mars wait here.

DEDUCTION

story A

A crow was very thirsty and wanted a drink of water.   She could not see a pool of water anywhere.   She flew round and round.   Then she saw a big jug outside a house.

The crow flew down to the jug.   She looked inside.   There was a little water at the bottom of the jug.

She could not reach the water with her beak.   She climbed onto the jug.   She almost fell into it, but she could not put her beak into the water.

She tried to break it with her beak.   But the jug was too strong.

She tried to knock it over, so that the water would run out onto the ground.   But the jug was too heavy.   It did not fall over.   Now the crow was very tired.   She thought she was going to die of thirst.

Then she had an idea.   She saw some stones lying on the ground.   She picked up a stone in her beak and dropped it into the jug.   Then another, and another.   The water rose higher every time a stone fell into the jug.

Soon the jug was nearly full of stones.   The water came to the top.   Then the clever crow had her drink.

story B

The big, black raven wanted a drink.

She saw a big jug with water at the bottom. She could not reach the water and wondered what to do.

"I know," she said. "I shall put some stones in the jug. Then the water will come up to the top."

After the first stone, the water rose a little. Then she put in another stone, and the water rose more.

She put more and more stones in until the water came up to the top of the jug.

"Now I can reach the water. At last I can have a drink," said the raven.

So she had a very long drink.

Moral:
If you try hard enough, you may find you can do something that at first seems very difficult.

> **What to do**
>
> Copy the table and fill it in.
> The first one has been done.

		story A	story B
1.	The bird was thirsty.	✓	✓
2.	The bird was a female.		
3.	The bird was a crow.		
4.	The bird was a raven.		
5.	The bird almost fell into the jug.		
6.	The bird was helped by another animal.		
7.	It was a hot day.		
8.	The jug was big.		
9.	The bird tried to break the jug.		
10.	The bird thought she would die of thirst.		

COMPARISONS

Mrs Porter and Mr Richards were neighbours.
Mrs Porter had to go away.   She asked Mr Richards if he would look after her car while she was gone.
As soon as Mrs Porter left town, Mr Richards took her car and sold it.

When Mrs Porter came back a few days later, she asked her neighbour what had happened to her car.

"I'm very sorry," said Mr Richards, "but your car was eaten by mice."

Mrs Porter said nothing.   She went home and worked out a plan to get her own back on her neighbour.

Mr Richards had a little boy called Billy.   The next day, Billy was playing ball outside Mrs Porter's front gate.   Mrs Porter took the little boy inside her house and hid him.

Mr Richards was very upset when he heard his son was lost.   He looked everywhere for the boy.   He went to Mrs Porter's house and said:

"Have you see my son Billy?"

"Yes," said Mrs Porter.   "He was playing outside my front gate yesterday.   A great big bird came down from out of the sky, picked him up and carried him away."

Now Mr Richards was very angry.   He said:

"Don't you make fun of me!   A bird could not pick up a child."

Mrs Porter smiled and said:

"I am not making fun of you.   If mice can eat a car, then a bird can pick up a little boy."

Then Mr Richards understood.   He told his neighbour that he had sold her car.   He gave Mrs Porter twice the money he got by selling the car, and Mrs Porter gave him back his son Billy.

Only one summary tells you exactly what happened in the story. Which is the best summary? Say what is wrong with the other four summaries.

1. Mrs Porter and Mr Richards went on holiday. While they were away, Billy's mice ate their cars.

2. Mrs Porter's car was eaten by mice. Mr Richards' son, Billy, was stolen by a big bird.

3. Mrs Porter kidnapped her neighbour's son, Billy. She gave him back and got a big reward.

4. Mr Richards sold Mrs Porter's car. Mrs Porter kidnapped Mr Richards' son. She swapped the boy for twice the cost of her car.

5. Mr Richards' son, Billy, stole Mrs Porter's car. Then the car was eaten by mice.

SUMMARY

1. Planet Skab is deep in space.

2. It is flat all over.

3. The weather is the same every day.

4. The nights on Skab are very cold.   During the night the planet is covered in ice.

5. At 10 o'clock in the morning, hailstones the size of golf balls fall from the sky.

6. By mid-day, all the hailstones and ice have melted in the hot sun. This makes the planet like a swamp.

7. On Skab all the plants grow very quickly.

8. By 4 o'clock in the afternoon, the swamps are full of green plants. These plants grow very close together and have sharp thorns.

9. Birds with sharp claws drop out of the sky.   They land on your shoulders.   They soon fly away if you give them some bird seed.

10. The light on Skab is very bright.   It hurts your eyes.

11. There is very little gravity on Skab.

12. The air on Skab is like the air on Earth.

What to do

Design a space suit for a man or woman on Skab.   Explorers must be able to walk about at any time, day or night.
Label it.   Give reasons why you have made it the way you have.

DRAWING

Facts about Pems and their habitat

1. Pems live on an island.
2. They live on nuts.
3. The nuts have very thick shells with very sharp spikes.
4. Pems cannot climb trees.
5. When the Pem shakes a nut tree, drops of poison fall from the branches.
6. Pems get water from holes in the ground.   These holes are deep and narrow; too narrow for Pems to enter.
7. The surface of the island is smooth and slippery like glass.
8. Pems live in caves.
9. At night they hang from the smooth ceilings of the caves.
10. Pems cannot see.
11. Pems have very good hearing.
12. If you turn a Pem over on its back, it has difficulty turning over.
13. Pems cannot fly.
14. Pems are very strong.
15. Pems are marsupials.

What to do

What do you think a Pem looks like?
Draw a Pem.   Label your drawing.   Say why you have drawn the Pem this way.

DRAWING

What would you call:

1. a boy who cries a lot?
2. a father who is always cross?
3. a pond where pythons live?
4. a stream that makes you very cold if you fall in it?
5. the very thin wife of a king?
6. something chickens use to write with?
7. something you might use in Art that would be hard to see?
8. a boy or girl that is very naughty?
9. a cat or dog that has been out in the rain?

a wet pet!

a wild child!

a snake lake!

a mad dad!

a shiver river!

a hen pen!

faint paint!

a lean queen!

a sad lad!

10. a very tidy road?
11. a small hen that is ill?
12. a very bad smell?
13. a chocolate you would give to a budgie to make him sing?
14. a plant for your garden that you do *not* have to pay for?
15. a football team with one man missing?
16. part of a house with a very high ceiling?
17. a mountain that does not move?
18. something in the sky a long way off?

A fox was very hungry. He looked everywhere for something to eat. He saw a hedgehog eating a mouse. The fox grabbed the mouse and ate it. The hedgehog was cross. She said:

"I hope you choke on it!"

The fox just laughed and said:

"Why do you look so silly?
You look like a pin cushion."

The hedgehog said:

"I need my prickles to protect myself."

"You poor thing," said the fox. "I don't need anything like that, because I'm clever."

Suddenly they heard a noise. Two dogs came out of the woods. The hedgehog rolled herself up into a ball. The fox ran away.

The two dogs sniffed at the hedgehog but soon left with pricked noses. They ran after the fox. The fox played a hundred and one tricks but he could not get away from the dogs. They caught him and killed him.

What to do

Only one summary tells you exactly what happened in the story. Which is the best summary? Say what is wrong with the other four summaries.

---

1. This is a story about a big-headed fox. He won't help his friend the hedgehog when she chokes.
2. This is a story about a big-headed fox who laughs at the hedgehog's prickles. The prickles save the hedgehog from some dogs. The fox gets caught and killed.
3. This is a story about a greedy fox who steals from a hedgehog. The hedgehog is eaten by some dogs.
4. This is a story about a nasty fox who tries to eat a hedgehog. The hedgehog is saved by her prickles.
5. This is a story about some dogs who chase a fox. The dogs saw a hedgehog. They ate the hedgehog and the fox.

SUMMARY

TIM TOM

What to do

Say if these pairs of sentences have the same or different meanings.

1. "Get off my bike, Linda," said Debbie.
   Linda told Debbie to get off her bike.

2. "Have you had your tea, Andy?" said Kev.
   Kev asked Andy to stay to tea.

3. "Mum, shall we paint the door white?" said Clive.
   Clive told his mum to paint the door white.

4. The girl sat near the old lady.
   The old lady was sitting beside the girl.

5. The dog ate the cake.
   The cake was taken by the dog.

6. The boy hid from his mum.
   The mum could not see her son.

7. "Come here at once, Linda!" said Sally.
   "Linda, come here now!" Sally said.

8. The tree fell across the road.
   The road fell onto the tree.

9. Linda gave Debbie half her cake.
   The two girls had equal shares.

10. We have to go now.
    We must not stay.

What to do

Copy the table and complete it.

	meaning	
	same	different
1		✓
2		
3		
4		
5		
6		
7		
8		
9		
10		

COMPARISONS